Fluency in Number Facts

Years 1 & 2

Peter Clarke

William Collins' dream of knowledge for all began with the publication of his first book in 1819. A self-educated mill worker, he not only enriched millions of lives, but also founded a flourishing publishing house. Today, staying true to this spirit, Collins books are packed with inspiration, innovation and practical expertise. They place you at the centre of a world of possibility and give you exactly what you need to explore it.

Collins. Freedom to teach.

Published by Collins

An imprint of HarperCollins*Publishers*
77–85 Fulham Palace Road
Hammersmith
London
W6 8JB

Browse the complete Collins catalogue at
www.collins.co.uk

© HarperCollins*Publishers* Limited 2013

10 9 8 7 6 5 4 3 2 1

ISBN-978-0-00-753130-1

The authors assert their moral rights to be identified as the authors of this work

British Library Cataloguing in Publication Data
A Catalogue record for this publication is available from the British Library

Edited by Gaynor Spry
Cover design by Nikki Kenwood
Cover artwork by Gwyneth Williams
Internal design by Nikki Kenwood
Illustrations by Andy Robb and Jouve
Typeset by Jouve

Printed by L.E.G.O. S.p.A. - Italy

Acknowledgement
The author wishes to thank Brian Molyneaux for his valuable contribution to this publication.

Contents

Addition and subtraction number facts to 20

Number facts for 0

$0 + 0 = 0$	$0 - 0 = 0$

Number facts for 1

$1 + 0 = 1$	$1 - 0 = 1$
$0 + 1 = 1$	$1 - 1 = 0$

Number facts for 2

$2 + 0 = 2$	$2 - 0 = 2$
$1 + 1 = 2$	$2 - 1 = 1$
$0 + 2 = 2$	$2 - 2 = 0$

Number facts for 3

$3 + 0 = 3$	$3 - 0 = 3$
$2 + 1 = 3$	$3 - 1 = 2$
$1 + 2 = 3$	$3 - 2 = 1$
$0 + 3 = 3$	$3 - 3 = 0$

Number facts for 4

$4 + 0 = 4$	$4 - 0 = 4$
$3 + 1 = 4$	$4 - 1 = 3$
$2 + 2 = 4$	$4 - 2 = 2$
$1 + 3 = 4$	$4 - 3 = 1$
$0 + 4 = 4$	$4 - 4 = 0$

Number facts for 5

$5 + 0 = 5$	$5 - 0 = 5$
$4 + 1 = 5$	$5 - 1 = 4$
$3 + 2 = 5$	$5 - 2 = 3$
$2 + 3 = 5$	$5 - 3 = 2$
$1 + 4 = 5$	$5 - 4 = 1$
$0 + 5 = 5$	$5 - 5 = 0$

Number facts for 6

$6 + 0 = 6$	$6 - 0 = 6$
$5 + 1 = 6$	$6 - 1 = 5$
$4 + 2 = 6$	$6 - 2 = 4$
$3 + 3 = 6$	$6 - 3 = 3$
$2 + 4 = 6$	$6 - 4 = 2$
$1 + 5 = 6$	$6 - 5 = 1$
$0 + 6 = 6$	$6 - 6 = 0$

Number facts for 7

$7 + 0 = 7$	$7 - 0 = 7$
$6 + 1 = 7$	$7 - 1 = 6$
$5 + 2 = 7$	$7 - 2 = 5$
$4 + 3 = 7$	$7 - 3 = 4$
$3 + 4 = 7$	$7 - 4 = 3$
$2 + 5 = 7$	$7 - 5 = 2$
$1 + 6 = 7$	$7 - 6 = 1$
$0 + 7 = 7$	$7 - 7 = 0$

Number facts for 8

$8 + 0 = 8$	$8 - 0 = 8$
$7 + 1 = 8$	$8 - 1 = 7$
$6 + 2 = 8$	$8 - 2 = 6$
$5 + 3 = 8$	$8 - 3 = 5$
$4 + 4 = 8$	$8 - 4 = 4$
$3 + 5 = 8$	$8 - 5 = 3$
$2 + 6 = 8$	$8 - 6 = 2$
$1 + 7 = 8$	$8 - 7 = 1$
$0 + 8 = 8$	$8 - 8 = 0$

Number facts for 9

$9 + 0 = 9$	$9 - 0 = 9$
$8 + 1 = 9$	$9 - 1 = 8$
$7 + 2 = 9$	$9 - 2 = 7$
$6 + 3 = 9$	$9 - 3 = 6$
$5 + 4 = 9$	$9 - 4 = 5$
$4 + 5 = 9$	$9 - 5 = 4$
$3 + 6 = 9$	$9 - 6 = 3$
$2 + 7 = 9$	$9 - 7 = 2$
$1 + 8 = 9$	$9 - 8 = 1$
$0 + 9 = 9$	$9 - 9 = 0$

Number facts for 10

$10 + 0 = 10$	$10 - 0 = 10$
$9 + 1 = 10$	$10 - 1 = 9$
$8 + 2 = 10$	$10 - 2 = 8$
$7 + 3 = 10$	$10 - 3 = 7$
$6 + 4 = 10$	$10 - 4 = 6$
$5 + 5 = 10$	$10 - 5 = 5$
$4 + 6 = 10$	$10 - 6 = 4$
$3 + 7 = 10$	$10 - 7 = 3$
$2 + 8 = 10$	$10 - 8 = 2$
$1 + 9 = 10$	$10 - 9 = 1$
$0 + 10 = 10$	$10 - 10 = 0$

Number facts for 11

$11 + 0 = 11$	$11 - 0 = 11$
$10 + 1 = 11$	$11 - 1 = 10$
$9 + 2 = 11$	$11 - 2 = 9$
$8 + 3 = 11$	$11 - 3 = 8$
$7 + 4 = 11$	$11 - 4 = 7$
$6 + 5 = 11$	$11 - 5 = 6$
$5 + 6 = 11$	$11 - 6 = 5$
$4 + 7 = 11$	$11 - 7 = 4$
$3 + 8 = 11$	$11 - 8 = 3$
$2 + 9 = 11$	$11 - 9 = 2$
$1 + 10 = 11$	$11 - 10 = 1$
$0 + 11 = 11$	$11 - 11 = 0$

Number facts for 12

12 + 0 = 12	12 − 0 = 12
11 + 1 = 12	12 − 1 = 11
10 + 2 = 12	12 − 2 = 10
9 + 3 = 12	12 − 3 = 9
8 + 4 = 12	12 − 4 = 8
7 + 5 = 12	12 − 5 = 7
6 + 6 = 12	12 − 6 = 6
5 + 7 = 12	12 − 7 = 5
4 + 8 = 12	12 − 8 = 4
3 + 9 = 12	12 − 9 = 3
2 + 10 = 12	12 − 10 = 2
1 + 11 = 12	12 − 11 = 1
0 + 12 = 12	12 − 12 = 0

Number facts for 13

13 + 0 = 13	13 − 0 = 13
12 + 1 = 13	13 − 1 = 12
11 + 2 = 13	13 − 2 = 11
10 + 3 = 13	13 − 3 = 10
9 + 4 = 13	13 − 4 = 9
8 + 5 = 13	13 − 5 = 8
7 + 6 = 13	13 − 6 = 7
6 + 7 = 13	13 − 7 = 6
5 + 8 = 13	13 − 8 = 5
4 + 9 = 13	13 − 9 = 4
3 + 10 = 13	13 − 10 = 3
2 + 11 = 13	13 − 11 = 2
1 + 12 = 13	13 − 12 = 1
0 + 13 = 13	13 − 13 = 0

Number facts for 14

14 + 0 = 14	14 − 0 = 14
13 + 1 = 14	14 − 1 = 13
12 + 2 = 14	14 − 2 = 12
11 + 3 = 14	14 − 3 = 11
10 + 4 = 14	14 − 4 = 10
9 + 5 = 14	14 − 5 = 9
8 + 6 = 14	14 − 6 = 8
7 + 7 = 14	14 − 7 = 7
6 + 8 = 14	14 − 8 = 6
5 + 9 = 14	14 − 9 = 5
4 + 10 = 14	14 − 10 = 4
3 + 11 = 14	14 − 11 = 3
2 + 12 = 14	14 − 12 = 2
1 + 13 = 14	14 − 13 = 1
0 + 14 = 14	14 − 14 = 0

Number facts for 15

15 + 0 = 15	15 − 0 = 15
14 + 1 = 15	15 − 1 = 14
13 + 2 = 15	15 − 2 = 13
12 + 3 = 15	15 − 3 = 12
11 + 4 = 15	15 − 4 = 11
10 + 5 = 15	15 − 5 = 10
9 + 6 = 15	15 − 6 = 9
8 + 7 = 15	15 − 7 = 8
7 + 8 = 15	15 − 8 = 7
6 + 9 = 15	15 − 9 = 6
5 + 10 = 15	15 − 10 = 5
4 + 11 = 15	15 − 11 = 4
3 + 12 = 15	15 − 12 = 3
2 + 13 = 15	15 − 13 = 2
1 + 14 = 15	15 − 14 = 1
0 + 15 = 15	15 − 15 = 0

Number facts for 16

16 + 0 = 16	16 − 0 = 16
15 + 1 = 16	16 − 1 = 15
14 + 2 = 16	16 − 2 = 14
13 + 3 = 16	16 − 3 = 13
12 + 4 = 16	16 − 4 = 12
11 + 5 = 16	16 − 5 = 11
10 + 6 = 16	16 − 6 = 10
9 + 7 = 16	16 − 7 = 9
8 + 8 = 16	16 − 8 = 8
7 + 9 = 16	16 − 9 = 7
6 + 10 = 16	16 − 10 = 6
5 + 11 = 16	16 − 11 = 5
4 + 12 = 16	16 − 12 = 4
3 + 13 = 16	16 − 13 = 3
2 + 14 = 16	16 − 14 = 2
1 + 15 = 16	16 − 15 = 1
0 + 16 = 16	16 − 16 = 0

Number facts for 17

17 + 0 = 17	17 − 0 = 17
16 + 1 = 17	17 − 1 = 16
15 + 2 = 17	17 − 2 = 15
14 + 3 = 17	17 − 3 = 14
13 + 4 = 17	17 − 4 = 13
12 + 5 = 17	17 − 5 = 12
11 + 6 = 17	17 − 6 = 11
10 + 7 = 17	17 − 7 = 10
9 + 8 = 17	17 − 8 = 9
8 + 9 = 17	17 − 9 = 8
7 + 10 = 17	17 − 10 = 7
6 + 11 = 17	17 − 11 = 6
5 + 12 = 17	17 − 12 = 5
4 + 13 = 17	17 − 13 = 4
3 + 14 = 17	17 − 14 = 3
2 + 15 = 17	17 − 15 = 2
1 + 16 = 17	17 − 16 = 1
0 + 17 = 17	17 − 17 = 0

Number facts for 18

18 + 0 = 18	18 − 0 = 18
17 + 1 = 18	18 − 1 = 17
16 + 2 = 18	18 − 2 = 16
15 + 3 = 18	18 − 3 = 15
14 + 4 = 18	18 − 4 = 14
13 + 5 = 18	18 − 5 = 13
12 + 6 = 18	18 − 6 = 12
11 + 7 = 18	18 − 7 = 11
10 + 8 = 18	18 − 8 = 10
9 + 9 = 18	18 − 9 = 9
8 + 10 = 18	18 − 10 = 8
7 + 11 = 18	18 − 11 = 7
6 + 12 = 18	18 − 12 = 6
5 + 13 = 18	18 − 13 = 5
4 + 14 = 18	18 − 14 = 4
3 + 15 = 18	18 − 15 = 3
2 + 16 = 18	18 − 16 = 2
1 + 17 = 18	18 − 17 = 1
0 + 18 = 18	18 − 18 = 0

Number facts for 19

19 + 0 = 19	19 − 0 = 19
18 + 1 = 19	19 − 1 = 18
17 + 2 = 19	19 − 2 = 17
16 + 3 = 19	19 − 3 = 16
15 + 4 = 19	19 − 4 = 15
14 + 5 = 19	19 − 5 = 14
13 + 6 = 19	19 − 6 = 13
12 + 7 = 19	19 − 7 = 12
11 + 8 = 19	19 − 8 = 11
10 + 9 = 19	19 − 9 = 10
9 + 10 = 19	19 − 10 = 9
8 + 11 = 19	19 − 11 = 8
7 + 12 = 19	19 − 12 = 7
6 + 13 = 19	19 − 13 = 6
5 + 14 = 19	19 − 14 = 5
4 + 15 = 19	19 − 15 = 4
3 + 16 = 19	19 − 16 = 3
2 + 17 = 19	19 − 17 = 2
1 + 18 = 19	19 − 18 = 1
0 + 19 = 19	19 − 19 = 0

Number facts for 20

20 + 0 = 20	20 − 0 = 20
19 + 1 = 20	20 − 1 = 19
18 + 2 = 20	20 − 2 = 18
17 + 3 = 20	20 − 3 = 17
16 + 4 = 20	20 − 4 = 16
15 + 5 = 20	20 − 5 = 15
14 + 6 = 20	20 − 6 = 14
13 + 7 = 20	20 − 7 = 13
12 + 8 = 20	20 − 8 = 12
11 + 9 = 20	20 − 9 = 11
10 + 10 = 20	20 − 10 = 10
9 + 11 = 20	20 − 11 = 9
8 + 12 = 20	20 − 12 = 8
7 + 13 = 20	20 − 13 = 7
6 + 14 = 20	20 − 14 = 6
5 + 15 = 20	20 − 15 = 5
4 + 16 = 20	20 − 16 = 4
3 + 17 = 20	20 − 17 = 3
2 + 18 = 20	20 − 18 = 2
1 + 19 = 20	20 − 19 = 1
0 + 20 = 20	20 − 20 = 0

Addition and subtraction trios to 20

Trios for 2

2 + 0 = 2
0 + 2 = 2
2 − 0 = 2
2 − 2 = 0

1 + 1 = 2
2 − 1 = 1

Trios for 3

3 + 0 = 3
0 + 3 = 3
3 − 0 = 3
3 − 3 = 0

2 + 1 = 3
1 + 2 = 3
3 − 1 = 2
3 − 2 = 1

Trios for 4

4 + 0 = 4
0 + 4 = 4
4 − 0 = 4
4 − 4 = 0

3 + 1 = 4
1 + 3 = 4
4 − 1 = 3
4 − 3 = 1

2 + 2 = 4
4 − 2 = 2

Trios for 5

5 + 0 = 5
0 + 5 = 5
5 − 0 = 5
5 − 5 = 0

4 + 1 = 5
1 + 4 = 5
5 − 1 = 4
5 − 4 = 1

3 + 2 = 5
2 + 3 = 5
5 − 2 = 3
5 − 3 = 2

Trios for 6

6 + 0 = 6
0 + 6 = 6
6 − 0 = 6
6 − 6 = 0

5 + 1 = 6
1 + 5 = 6
6 − 1 = 5
6 − 5 = 1

4 + 2 = 6
2 + 4 = 6
6 − 2 = 4
6 − 4 = 2

3 + 3 = 6
6 − 3 = 3

Trios for 7

7 + 0 = 7
0 + 7 = 7
7 − 0 = 7
7 − 7 = 0

6 + 1 = 7
1 + 6 = 7
7 − 1 = 6
7 − 6 = 1

5 + 2 = 7
2 + 5 = 7
7 − 2 = 5
7 − 5 = 2

4 + 3 = 7
3 + 4 = 7
7 − 3 = 4
7 − 4 = 3

Trios for 8

8 + 0 = 8
0 + 8 = 8
8 − 0 = 8
8 − 8 = 0

7 + 1 = 8
1 + 7 = 8
8 − 1 = 7
8 − 7 = 1

6 + 2 = 8
2 + 6 = 8
8 − 2 = 6
8 − 6 = 2

5 + 3 = 8
3 + 5 = 8
8 − 3 = 5
8 − 5 = 3

4 + 4 = 8
8 − 4 = 4

Trios for 9

9 + 0 = 9
0 + 9 = 9
9 − 0 = 9
9 − 9 = 0

8 + 1 = 9
1 + 8 = 9
9 − 1 = 8
9 − 8 = 1

7 + 2 = 9
2 + 7 = 9
9 − 2 = 7
9 − 7 = 2

6 + 3 = 9
3 + 6 = 9
9 − 3 = 6
9 − 6 = 3

5 + 4 = 9
4 + 5 = 9
9 − 4 = 5
9 − 5 = 4

Trios for 10

10 + 0 = 10
0 + 10 = 10
10 − 0 = 10
10 − 10 = 0

```
    10
  0    10
```

9 + 1 = 10
1 + 9 = 10
10 − 1 = 9
10 − 9 = 1

```
    10
  1    9
```

8 + 2 = 10
2 + 8 = 10
10 − 2 = 8
10 − 8 = 2

```
    10
  2    8
```

7 + 3 = 10
3 + 7 = 10
10 − 3 = 7
10 − 7 = 3

```
    10
  3    7
```

6 + 4 = 10
4 + 6 = 10
10 − 4 = 6
10 − 6 = 4

```
    10
  4    6
```

5 + 5 = 10
10 − 5 = 5

```
    10
  5    5
```

Trios for 11

11 + 0 = 11
0 + 11 = 11
11 − 0 = 11
11 − 11 = 0

```
    11
  0    11
```

10 + 1 = 11
1 + 10 = 11
11 − 1 = 10
11 − 10 = 1

```
    11
  1    10
```

9 + 2 = 11
2 + 9 = 11
11 − 2 = 9
11 − 9 = 2

```
    11
  2    9
```

8 + 3 = 11
3 + 8 = 11
11 − 3 = 8
11 − 8 = 3

```
    11
  3    8
```

7 + 4 = 11
4 + 7 = 11
11 − 4 = 7
11 − 7 = 4

```
    11
  4    7
```

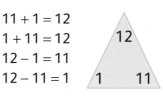

6 + 5 = 11
5 + 6 = 11
11 − 5 = 6
11 − 6 = 5

```
    11
  5    6
```

Trios for 12

12 + 0 = 12
0 + 12 = 12
12 − 0 = 12
12 − 12 = 0

```
    12
  0    12
```

11 + 1 = 12
1 + 11 = 12
12 − 1 = 11
12 − 11 = 1

```
    12
  1    11
```

10 + 2 = 12
2 + 10 = 12
12 − 2 = 10
12 − 10 = 2

```
    12
  2    10
```

9 + 3 = 12
3 + 9 = 12
12 − 3 = 9
12 − 9 = 3

```
    12
  3    9
```

8 + 4 = 12
4 + 8 = 12
12 − 4 = 8
12 − 8 = 4

```
    12
  4    8
```

7 + 5 = 12
5 + 7 = 12
12 − 5 = 7
12 − 7 = 5

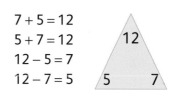

6 + 6 = 12
12 − 6 = 6

```
    12
  6    6
```

Trios for 13

13 + 0 = 13
0 + 13 = 13
13 − 0 = 13
13 − 13 = 0

12 + 1 = 13
1 + 12 = 13
13 − 1 = 12
13 − 12 = 1
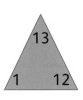

11 + 2 = 13
2 + 11 = 13
13 − 2 = 11
13 − 11 = 2

10 + 3 = 13
3 + 10 = 13
13 − 3 = 10
13 − 10 = 3

9 + 4 = 13
4 + 9 = 13
13 − 4 = 9
13 − 9 = 4

8 + 5 = 13
5 + 8 = 13
13 − 5 = 8
13 − 8 = 5

7 + 6 = 13
6 + 7 = 13
13 − 6 = 7
13 − 7 = 6

Trios for 14

14 + 0 = 14
0 + 14 = 14
14 − 0 = 14
14 − 14 = 0

13 + 1 = 14
1 + 13 = 14
14 − 1 = 13
14 − 13 = 1

12 + 2 = 14
2 + 12 = 14
14 − 2 = 12
14 − 12 = 2

11 + 3 = 14
3 + 11 = 14
14 − 3 = 11
14 − 11 = 3

10 + 4 = 14
4 + 10 = 14
14 − 4 = 10
14 − 10 = 4

9 + 5 = 14
5 + 9 = 14
14 − 5 = 9
14 − 9 = 5
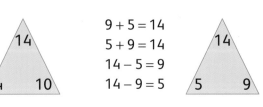

8 + 6 = 14
6 + 8 = 14
14 − 6 = 8
14 − 8 = 6
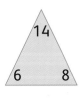

7 + 7 = 14
14 − 7 = 7

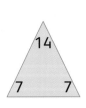

Trios for 15

15 + 0 = 15
0 + 15 = 15
15 − 0 = 15
15 − 15 = 0

14 + 1 = 15
1 + 14 = 15
15 − 1 = 14
15 − 14 = 1

13 + 2 = 15
2 + 13 = 15
15 − 2 = 13
15 − 13 = 2

12 + 3 = 15
3 + 12 = 15
15 − 3 = 12
15 − 12 = 3

11 + 4 = 15
4 + 11 = 15
15 − 4 = 11
15 − 11 = 4

10 + 5 = 15
5 + 10 = 15
15 − 5 = 10
15 − 10 = 5

9 + 6 = 15
6 + 9 = 15
15 − 6 = 9
15 − 9 = 6

8 + 7 = 15
7 + 8 = 15
15 − 7 = 8
15 − 8 = 7

Trios for 16

16 + 0 = 16
0 + 16 = 16
16 − 0 = 16
16 − 16 = 0

15 + 1 = 16
1 + 15 = 16
16 − 1 = 15
16 − 15 = 1

14 + 2 = 16
2 + 14 = 16
16 − 2 = 14
16 − 14 = 2

13 + 3 = 16
3 + 13 = 16
16 − 3 = 13
16 − 13 = 3

12 + 4 = 16
4 + 12 = 16
16 − 4 = 12
16 − 12 = 4

11 + 5 = 16
5 + 11 = 16
16 − 5 = 11
16 − 11 = 5

10 + 6 = 16
6 + 10 = 16
16 − 6 = 10
16 − 10 = 6

9 + 7 = 16
7 + 9 = 16
16 − 7 = 9
16 − 9 = 7

8 + 8 = 16
16 − 8 = 8

Trios for 17

17 + 0 = 17
0 + 17 = 17
17 − 0 = 17
17 − 17 = 0

16 + 1 = 17
1 + 16 = 17
17 − 1 = 16
17 − 16 = 1

15 + 2 = 17
2 + 15 = 17
17 − 2 = 15
17 − 15 = 2

14 + 3 = 17
3 + 14 = 17
17 − 3 = 14
17 − 14 = 3

13 + 4 = 17
4 + 13 = 17
17 − 4 = 13
17 − 13 = 4

12 + 5 = 17
5 + 12 = 17
17 − 5 = 12
17 − 12 = 5

11 + 6 = 17
6 + 11 = 17
17 − 6 = 11
17 − 11 = 6

10 + 7 = 17
7 + 10 = 17
17 − 7 = 10
17 − 10 = 7

9 + 8 = 17
8 + 9 = 17
17 − 8 = 9
17 − 9 = 8

Trios for 18

18 + 0 = 18
0 + 18 = 18
18 − 0 = 18
18 − 18 = 0

17 + 1 = 18
1 + 17 = 18
18 − 1 = 17
18 − 17 = 1

16 + 2 = 18
2 + 16 = 18
18 − 2 = 16
18 − 16 = 2

15 + 3 = 18
3 + 15 = 18
18 − 3 = 15
18 − 15 = 3

14 + 4 = 18
4 + 14 = 18
18 − 4 = 14
18 − 14 = 4

13 + 5 = 18
5 + 13 = 18
18 − 5 = 13
18 − 13 = 5

12 + 6 = 18
6 + 12 = 18
18 − 6 = 12
18 − 12 = 6

11 + 7 = 18
7 + 11 = 18
18 − 7 = 11
18 − 11 = 7

10 + 8 = 18
8 + 10 = 18
18 − 8 = 10

18 − 10 = 8

9 + 9 = 18
18 − 9 = 9

Trios for 19

19 + 0 = 19
0 + 19 = 19
19 − 0 = 19
19 − 19 = 0

18 + 1 = 19
1 + 18 = 19
19 − 1 = 18
19 − 18 = 1

17 + 2 = 19
2 + 17 = 19
19 − 2 = 17
19 − 17 = 2

16 + 3 = 19
3 + 16 = 19
19 − 3 = 16
19 − 16 = 3

15 + 4 = 19
4 + 15 = 19
19 − 4 = 15
19 − 15 = 4

14 + 5 = 19
5 + 14 = 19
19 − 5 = 14
19 − 14 = 5

13 + 6 = 19
6 + 13 = 19
19 − 6 = 13
19 − 13 = 6

12 + 7 = 19
7 + 12 = 19
19 − 7 = 12
19 − 12 = 7

11 + 8 = 19
8 + 11 = 19
19 − 8 = 11
19 − 11 = 8

10 + 9 = 19
9 + 10 = 19
19 − 9 = 10
19 − 10 = 9

Trios for 20

20 + 0 = 20
0 + 20 = 20
20 − 0 = 20
20 − 20 = 0

19 + 1 = 20
1 + 19 = 20
20 − 1 = 19
20 − 19 = 1

18 + 2 = 20
2 + 18 = 20
20 − 2 = 18
20 − 18 = 2

17 + 3 = 20
3 + 17 = 20
20 − 3 = 17
20 − 17 = 3

16 + 4 = 20
4 + 16 = 20
20 − 4 = 16
20 − 16 = 4

15 + 5 = 20
5 + 15 = 20
20 − 5 = 15
20 − 15 = 5

14 + 6 = 20
6 + 14 = 20
20 − 6 = 14
20 − 14 = 6

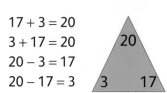

13 + 7 = 20
7 + 13 = 20
20 − 7 = 13
20 − 13 = 7

12 + 8 = 20
8 + 12 = 20
20 − 8 = 12
20 − 12 = 8

11 + 9 = 20
9 + 11 = 20
20 − 9 = 11
20 − 11 = 9

10 + 10 = 20
20 − 10 = 10

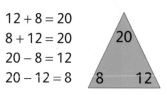

Addition number facts to **5**, **10** and **20** table

Addition can be done in any order.

So, $2 + 3 = 5$ and $3 + 2 = 5$

Addition is the opposite of subtraction.

So, if you know that $3 + 2 = 5$ you also know that:

$5 - 3 = 2$ and $5 - 2 = 3$

+	0	1	2	3	4	5	6	7	8	9	10
0	0	1	2	3	4	5	6	7	8	9	10
1	1	2	3	4	5	6	7	8	9	10	11
2	2	3	4	5	6	7	8	9	10	11	12
3	3	4	5	6	7	8	9	10	11	12	13
4	4	5	6	7	8	9	10	11	12	13	14
5	5	6	7	8	9	10	11	12	13	14	15
6	6	7	8	9	10	11	12	13	14	15	16
7	7	8	9	10	11	12	13	14	15	16	17
8	8	9	10	11	12	13	14	15	16	17	18
9	9	10	11	12	13	14	15	16	17	18	19
10	10	11	12	13	14	15	16	17	18	19	20

Addition of 1-digit and 2-digit numbers to 20 table

+	11	12	13	14	15	16	17	18	19	20
0	11	12	13	14	15	16	17	18	19	20
1	12	13	14	15	16	17	18	19	20	
2	13	14	15	16	17	18	19	20		
3	14	15	16	17	18	19	20			
4	15	16	17	18	19	20				
5	16	17	18	19	20					
6	17	18	19	20						
7	18	19	20							
8	19	20								
9	20									

2, 5 and 10 times tables facts

2 times table	5 times table	10 times table

 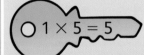 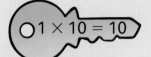

$1 \times 2 = 2$ $1 \times 5 = 5$ $1 \times 10 = 10$

$2 \times 2 = 4$ $2 \times 5 = 10$ $2 \times 10 = 20$

$3 \times 2 = 6$ $3 \times 5 = 15$ $3 \times 10 = 30$

$4 \times 2 = 8$ $4 \times 5 = 20$ $4 \times 10 = 40$

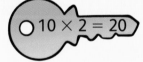 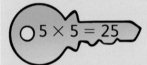 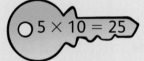

$5 \times 2 = 10$ $5 \times 5 = 25$ $5 \times 10 = 25$

$6 \times 2 = 12$ $6 \times 5 = 30$ $6 \times 10 = 60$

$7 \times 2 = 14$ $7 \times 5 = 35$ $7 \times 10 = 70$

$8 \times 2 = 16$ $8 \times 5 = 40$ $8 \times 10 = 80$

$9 \times 2 = 18$ $9 \times 5 = 45$ $9 \times 10 = 90$

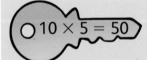

$10 \times 2 = 20$ $10 \times 5 = 50$ $10 \times 10 = 100$

$11 \times 2 = 22$ $11 \times 5 = 55$ $11 \times 10 = 110$

$12 \times 2 = 24$ $12 \times 5 = 60$ $12 \times 10 = 120$

Division facts relating to the **2**, **5** and **10** times tables facts

Division facts related to the 2 times table	Division facts related to the 5 times table	Division facts related to the 10 times table
$2 \div 2 = 1$	$5 \div 5 = 1$	$10 \div 10 = 1$
$4 \div 2 = 2$	$10 \div 5 = 2$	$20 \div 10 = 2$
$6 \div 2 = 3$	$15 \div 5 = 3$	$30 \div 10 = 3$
$8 \div 2 = 4$	$20 \div 5 = 4$	$40 \div 10 = 4$
$10 \div 2 = 5$	$25 \div 5 = 5$	$50 \div 10 = 5$
$12 \div 2 = 6$	$30 \div 5 = 6$	$60 \div 10 = 6$
$14 \div 2 = 7$	$35 \div 5 = 7$	$70 \div 10 = 7$
$16 \div 2 = 8$	$40 \div 5 = 8$	$80 \div 10 = 8$
$18 \div 2 = 9$	$45 \div 5 = 9$	$90 \div 10 = 9$
$20 \div 2 = 10$	$50 \div 5 = 10$	$100 \div 10 = 10$
$22 \div 2 = 11$	$55 \div 5 = 11$	$110 \div 10 = 11$
$24 \div 2 = 12$	$60 \div 5 = 12$	$120 \div 10 = 12$

Multiples of **2**, **5** and **10**

Multiples of 2

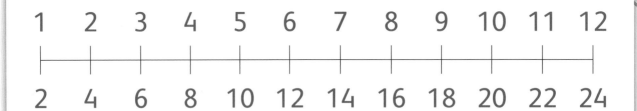

Multiples of 5

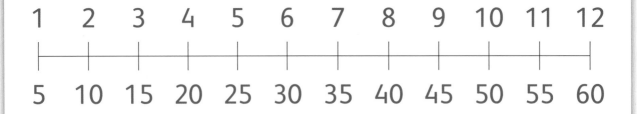

Multiples of 10

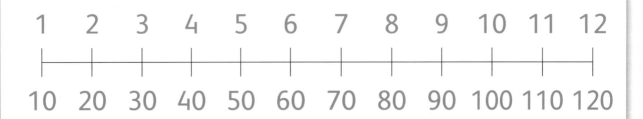

Fluency in Number Facts

2, 5 and 10 multiplication facts table

×	2	5	10
1	1×2	1×5	1×10
2	2×2	2×5	2×10
3	3×2	3×5	3×10
4	4×2	4×5	4×10
5	5×2	5×5	5×10
6	6×2	6×5	6×10
7	7×2	7×5	7×10
8	8×2	8×5	8×10
9	9×2	9×5	9×10
10	10×2	10×5	10×10
11	11×2	11×5	11×10
12	12×2	12×5	12×10

×	2	5	10
1	2	5	10
2	4	10	20
3	6	15	30
4	8	20	40
5	10	25	50
6	12	30	60
7	14	35	70
8	16	40	80
9	18	45	90
10	20	50	100
11	22	55	110
12	24	60	120

Fluency in Number Facts

Trios for the **2**, **5** and **10** times tables and the related division facts

2 times table and related division facts

$1 \times 2 = 2$
$2 \times 1 = 2$
$2 \div 2 = 1$
$2 \div 1 = 2$

$2 \times 2 = 4$
$4 \div 2 = 2$

$3 \times 2 = 6$
$2 \times 3 = 6$
$6 \div 2 = 3$
$6 \div 3 = 2$

$4 \times 2 = 8$
$2 \times 4 = 8$
$8 \div 2 = 4$
$8 \div 4 = 2$

$5 \times 2 = 10$
$2 \times 5 = 10$
$10 \div 2 = 5$
$10 \div 5 = 2$

$6 \times 2 = 12$
$2 \times 6 = 12$
$12 \div 2 = 6$
$12 \div 6 = 2$

$7 \times 2 = 14$
$2 \times 7 = 14$
$14 \div 2 = 7$
$14 \div 7 = 2$

$8 \times 2 = 16$
$2 \times 8 = 16$
$16 \div 2 = 8$
$16 \div 8 = 2$

$9 \times 2 = 18$
$2 \times 9 = 18$
$18 \div 2 = 9$
$18 \div 9 = 2$

$10 \times 2 = 20$
$2 \times 10 = 20$
$20 \div 2 = 10$
$20 \div 10 = 2$

$11 \times 2 = 22$
$2 \times 11 = 22$
$22 \div 2 = 11$
$22 \div 11 = 2$

$12 \times 2 = 24$
$2 \times 12 = 24$
$24 \div 2 = 12$
$24 \div 12 = 2$

21

5 times table and related division facts

$1 \times 5 = 5$
$5 \times 1 = 5$
$5 \div 5 = 1$
$5 \div 1 = 5$

5
1   5

$2 \times 5 = 10$
$5 \times 2 = 10$
$10 \div 5 = 2$
$10 \div 2 = 5$

10
2   5

$3 \times 5 = 15$
$5 \times 3 = 15$
$15 \div 5 = 3$
$15 \div 3 = 5$

15
3   5

$4 \times 5 = 20$
$5 \times 4 = 20$
$20 \div 5 = 4$
$20 \div 4 = 5$

20
4   5

$5 \times 5 = 25$
$25 \div 5 = 5$

25
5   5

$6 \times 5 = 30$
$5 \times 6 = 30$
$30 \div 5 = 6$
$30 \div 6 = 5$

30
6   5

$7 \times 5 = 35$
$5 \times 7 = 35$
$35 \div 5 = 7$
$35 \div 7 = 5$

35
7   5

$8 \times 5 = 40$
$5 \times 8 = 40$
$40 \div 5 = 8$
$40 \div 8 = 5$

40
8   5

$9 \times 5 = 45$
$5 \times 9 = 45$
$45 \div 5 = 9$
$45 \div 9 = 5$

45
9   5

$10 \times 5 = 50$
$5 \times 10 = 50$
$50 \div 5 = 10$
$50 \div 10 = 5$

50
10   5

$11 \times 5 = 55$
$5 \times 11 = 55$
$55 \div 5 = 11$
$55 \div 11 = 5$

55
11   5

$12 \times 5 = 60$
$5 \times 12 = 60$
$60 \div 5 = 12$
$60 \div 12 = 5$

60
12   5

10 times table and related division facts

$1 \times 10 = 10$
$10 \times 1 = 10$
$10 \div 10 = 1$
$10 \div 1 = 10$

$2 \times 10 = 20$
$10 \times 2 = 20$
$20 \div 10 = 2$
$20 \div 2 = 10$

$3 \times 10 = 30$
$10 \times 3 = 30$
$30 \div 10 = 3$
$30 \div 3 = 10$

$4 \times 10 = 40$
$10 \times 4 = 40$
$40 \div 10 = 4$
$40 \div 4 = 10$

$5 \times 10 = 50$
$10 \times 5 = 50$
$50 \div 10 = 5$
$50 \div 5 = 10$

$6 \times 10 = 60$
$10 \times 6 = 60$
$60 \div 10 = 6$
$60 \div 6 = 10$

$7 \times 10 = 70$
$10 \times 7 = 70$
$70 \div 10 = 7$
$70 \div 7 = 10$

$8 \times 10 = 80$
$10 \times 8 = 80$
$80 \div 10 = 8$
$80 \div 8 = 10$

$9 \times 10 = 90$
$10 \times 9 = 90$
$90 \div 10 = 9$
$90 \div 9 = 10$

$10 \times 10 = 100$
$100 \div 10 = 10$

$11 \times 10 = 110$
$10 \times 11 = 110$
$110 \div 10 = 11$
$110 \div 11 = 10$

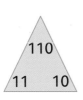

$12 \times 10 = 120$
$10 \times 12 = 120$
$120 \div 10 = 12$
$120 \div 12 = 10$

Read numbers to 100 in numerals

Compare numbers from 0 up to 100

Which monkey wins?: larger
A game for 2 players

You need:
- 30 counters

Before you start:
- Cover each of the numbers with a counter.

What to do:
- Each player removes a counter.
- The player that uncovers the larger number keeps both counters and says why.
- Keep going until all the counters have been removed.

The winner is:
- The player with more counters.

97 is larger than 18.

Variation
Which monkey wins?: smaller
- The player that uncovers the smaller number keeps both counters.

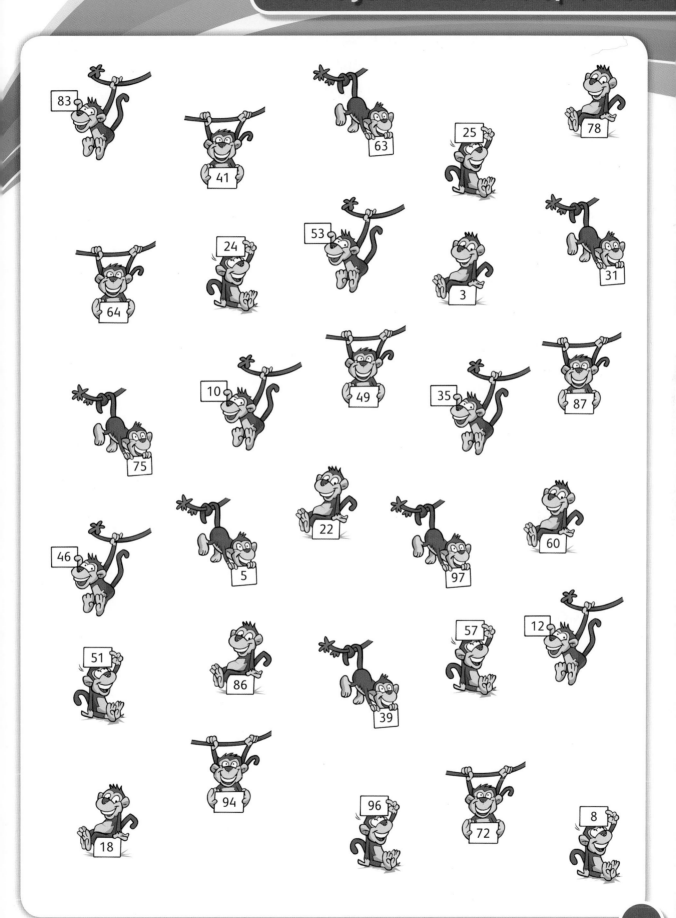

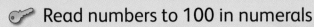

🔑 Read numbers to 100 in numerals

🔑 Recognise the place value of each digit in a 2-digit number (tens, ones)

🔑 Order numbers from 0 up to 100

Balloon numbers
A game for 2 players

You need:
- 2 sets of 0–9 number cards
- 18 counters: 9 of one colour, 9 of another colour

Before you start:
- Decide who will have which colour counters.
- Each player puts one of their counters on each balloon.
- Shuffle all the cards and place them face down in a pile.

Take turns to:
- pick the top two cards and place them on the 'tens' and 'ones' spaces to make a 2-digit number
- say the number and remove your counter from the balloon in the matching number range
- place the number cards to one side.

For example:

86 | 8 6

80–89

Golden rules
- If your counter has already been removed from the balloon, miss that turn.
- When all the cards have been used, reshuffle the cards, place them face down in a pile and continue the game.

The winner is:
- the first player to remove all of their counters from the balloons.

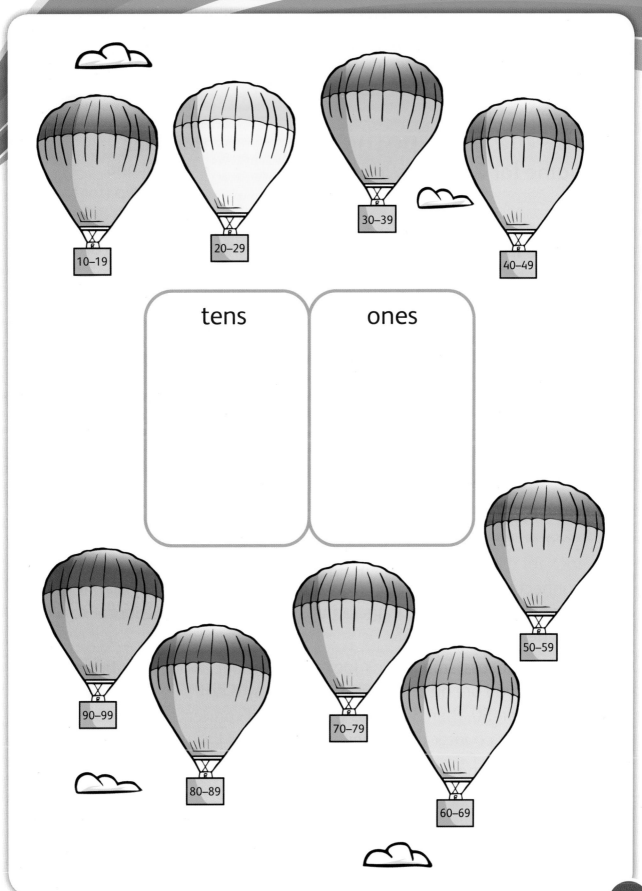

tens

ones

10–19 20–29 30–39 40–49 50–59 60–69 70–79 80–89 90–99

Fluency in Number Facts

Read numbers to 100 in numerals

 Compare numbers from 0 up to 100; use < and > signs

Take the right path
A game for 2 players

You need:
- pencil and paperclip (for the spinner)
- 2 counters of different colours

Before you start:
- Decide whether you are going to use the green spinner or the brown spinner.
- Decide who will have which colour counter.
- Put the counters on '50'.

Take turns to:
- spin the spinner and say the word or sign.

Golden rules

- If you spin *more, greater, larger* or >
look for a number that is more than the number you are on and connected to it by a path. For example, if you are on 50, then 65 is more than 50 and connected by a path. Move your counter to this new number, i.e. 65.

- If you spin *less, smaller* or < look for a number that is less than the number you are on and connected to it by a path. For example, if you are on 50, then 31 is less than 50 and connected by a path. Move your counter to this new number, i.e. 31.

- If you can't move, miss that turn.

The winner is:
- the first player to reach '100'.

🔑 Count in multiples of twos, fives and tens

Staircase counting
A game for 2 players

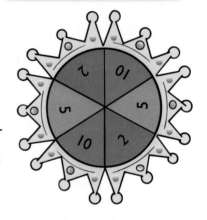

You need:
- pencil and paperclip (for the spinner)
- 36 counters

Before you start:
- Cover the numbers on each of the steps with a counter.

Take turns to:
- spin the spinner.

Golden rules
- Each time you spin a 2, walk up the red staircase, starting from Start. Say the number on each of the steps, until you reach the next step with a counter on it. Say the number you think is under this counter: then lift the counter and see if you are correct. If you are correct, keep the counter.

- Each time you spin a 5, walk up the blue staircase, starting from Start. Say the number on each of the steps, until you reach the next step with a counter on it. Say the number you think is under this counter: then lift the counter and see if you are correct. If you are correct, keep the counter.

- Each time you spin a 10, walk up the green staircase, starting from Start. Say the number on each of the steps, until you reach the next step with a counter on it. Say the number you think is under this counter: then lift the counter and see if you are correct. If you are correct, keep the counter.

Continue until:
- you have removed all of the counters from one of the staircases and reached the door.

The winner is:
- the player with more counters.

Count in multiples of twos, fives and tens

Courtyard counting
A game for 2 players

You need:
- button
- 2 counters of different colours
- 1–6 dice

Before you start:
- Decide whether you are both going to practise counting on in steps of 2, 5 or 10.
- Place the button on the person with that number to remind you of your counting pattern.
- Decide who will have which colour counter.
- Place the counters on 'Start'.

Take turns to:
- roll the dice
- move your counter that number of stones, to make sure you land on the next number in your chosen counting pattern.

Golden rules

- You can move sideways ↔, up and down ↕, or diagonally ↘, or a combination of these within a turn.
- You cannot step on the same stone twice within a turn.
- You can step on any stone, as long as the last number of each move is the next number in your chosen counting pattern.
- If you can't move to the next number in your chosen counting pattern, then miss that turn.

The counting pattern for 2 is 2, 4, 6...

The counting pattern for 5 is 5, 10, 15...

The counting pattern for 10 is 10, 20, 30...

20	15	40	5	60	14
8	30	2	10	30	35
4	40	Start		12	70
10	5			5	10
2	30	60	10	2	35
10	14	70	2	12	30

Counting in steps of 5!

The winner is the first player to reach any number:

- 20 if counting in steps of 2
- 50 if counting in steps of 5
- 100 if counting in steps of 10.

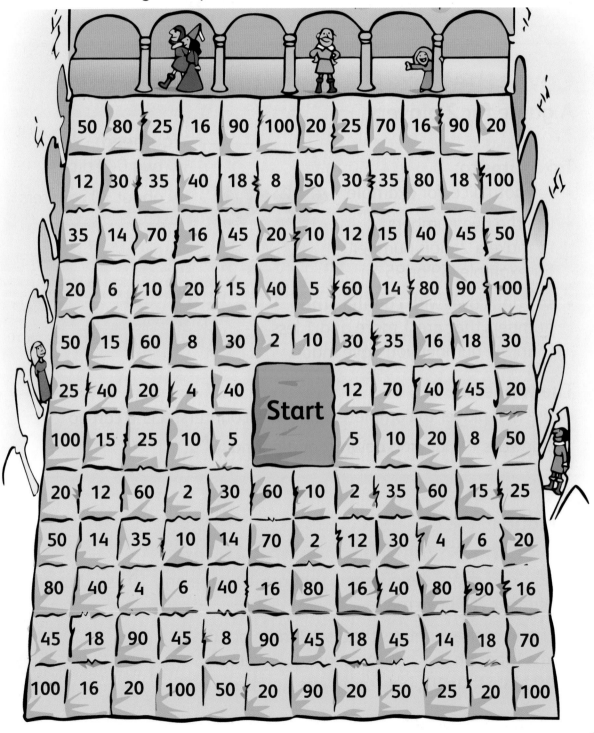

🗝 Read numbers to 100 in numerals

🗝 Recognise the place value of each digit in a 2-digit number (tens, ones)

🗝 Given a number, identify one more and one less

🗝 Given a number, identify 10 more and 10 less

Cover the boxes: 1 more and 1 less
A game for 2 players

Take turns to:

- roll both dice, for example:

- use the two numbers to make a 2-digit number, for example, 59 or 95

- say and cover with counters the numbers that are 1 more and 1 less than the number you have made.

> 60 is 1 more than 59.
> 58 is 1 less than 59.

You need:
- two 0–9 dice
- about 30 counters

The winner is:

- the first player to complete a line of 4 counters. A line can go sideways ↔, up and down ↕, or diagonally ↘.

Variation
Cover the boxes: 10 more and 10 less

- Say, and cover, the numbers that are 10 more and 10 less than the number you have made.

- If one of the numbers that is 10 more or 10 less is not on the 1–100 square, for example, 10 more than 95, only cover one number.

> 105 is 10 more than 95.
> 85 is 10 less than 95.

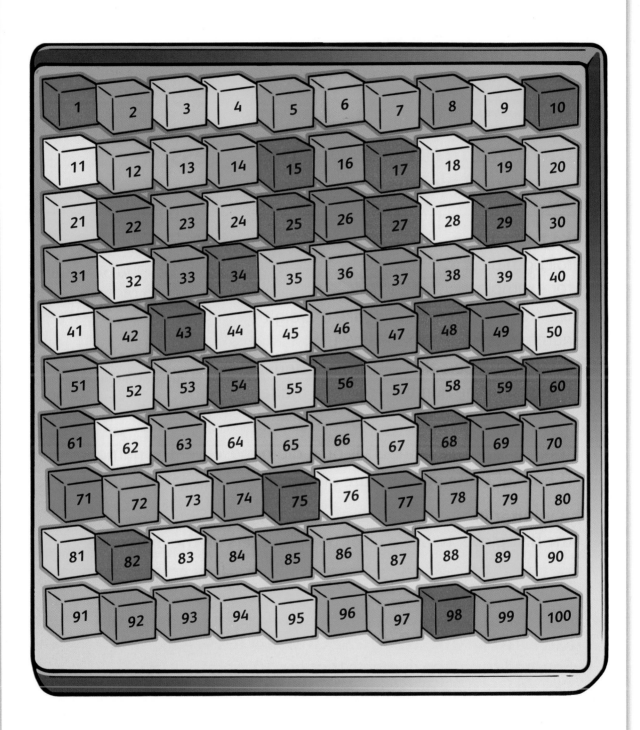

Fluency in Number Facts

🔑 Read numbers to 100 in numerals

🔑 Recognise the place value of each digit in a 2-digit number (tens, ones)

🔑 Given a number, identify one more and one less

🔑 Given a number, identify 10 more and 10 less

Diamond grab: 1 more and 1 less
A game for 2 players

You need:
- two 0–9 dice
- 10 counters: 5 for each player

Take turns to:
- roll both dice, for example:
- use the two numbers to make a 2-digit number, for example, 19 or 91
- say the numbers that are 1 more and 1 less than the number you have made.

> 92 is 1 more than 91.
> 90 is 1 less than 91.

Golden rules
- If either of these numbers is on a diamond, cover the number.
- If both of these numbers are on a diamond, cover both numbers.

The winner is:
- the first player to place all of their counters on the diamonds.

Variation
Diamond grab: 10 more and 10 less
- Say, and cover, the numbers that are 10 more and 10 less than the number you have made.

> 101 is 10 more than 91.
> 81 is 10 less than 91.

- If one of the numbers that is 10 more or 10 less is not on a diamond, for example, 10 more than 91, only cover one number.

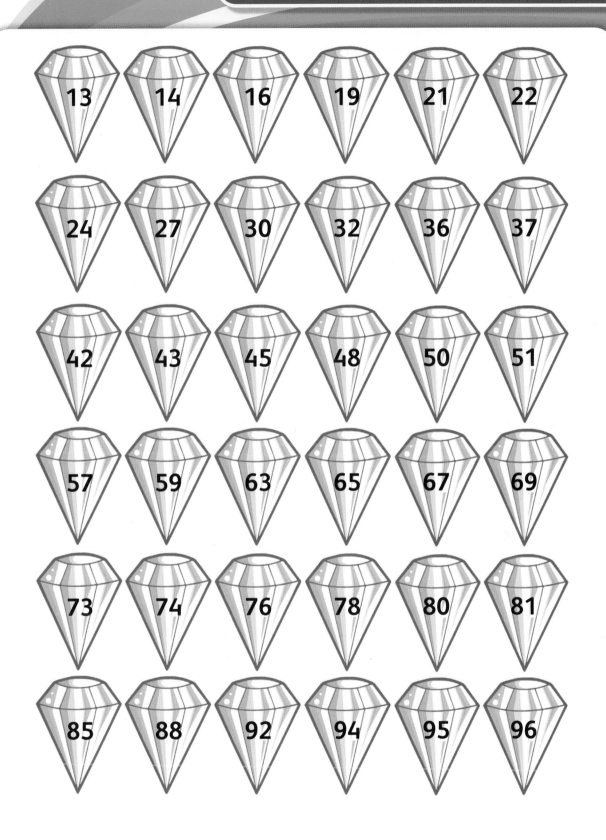

13 14 16 19 21 22

24 27 30 32 36 37

42 43 45 48 50 51

57 59 63 65 67 69

73 74 76 78 80 81

85 88 92 94 95 96

Fluency in Number Facts

Recall addition facts to 20 fluently

Firework additions
A game for 2 players

You need:
- two 0–9 dice
- 12 counters: 6 for each player

Take turns to:
- roll both dice
- add the two numbers together
- say the number sentence
- cover the answer using one of your counters.

> 5 add 3 equals 8

Golden rule
- If an answer is already covered, miss that turn.

The winner is:
- the first player to put all of their counters on 6 different numbers.

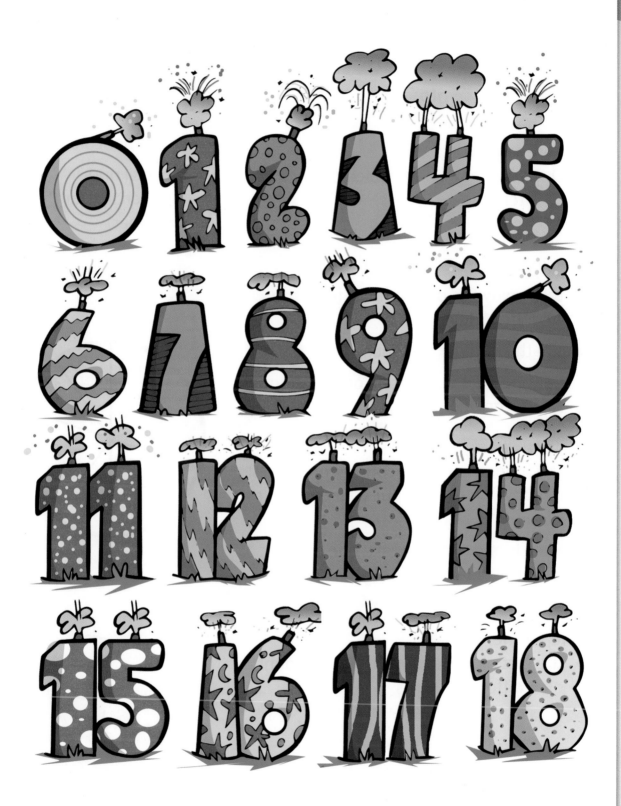

Recall subtraction facts to 20 fluently

Shipwreck subtractions
A game for 2 players

Before you start:
- Decide who will have which colour counters.

Take turns to:
- spin the spinner and roll the dice
- take away the dice number from the spinner number
- say the number sentence
- put one of your counters on the island that shows the answer.

Golden rules
- If your partner has a counter on that island already you can still put your counter on the island.
- Each island can only take one counter of each colour. If one of *your* counters is already on an island, miss that turn.

The winner is:
- the first player to put all of their counters on 7 different islands.

You need:
- 14 counters: 7 of one colour, 7 of another colour
- pencil and paperclip (for the spinner)
- 0–9 dice

Recall addition and subtraction facts to 20 fluently

Fruity facts
A game for 2 players

You need:
- 16 counters:
  8 of one colour, 8 of another colour
- two 0–9 dice

Before you start:
- Decide who will have which colour counters.

Take turns to:
- roll both dice

- add the two numbers together

  or

  take away the smaller number from the larger number

- say the number sentence

- put one of your counters on the bunch of cherries with the answer.

Golden rules
- If your partner has a counter on that bunch of cherries already you can still put one of your counters on the bunch of cherries.

- Each bunch of cherries can only take one counter of each colour. If one of *your* counters is already on a bunch of cherries, miss that turn.

- If you cannot find a bunch of cherries with your answer on it, miss that turn.

The winner is:
- the first player to put all of their counters on 8 different bunches of cherries.

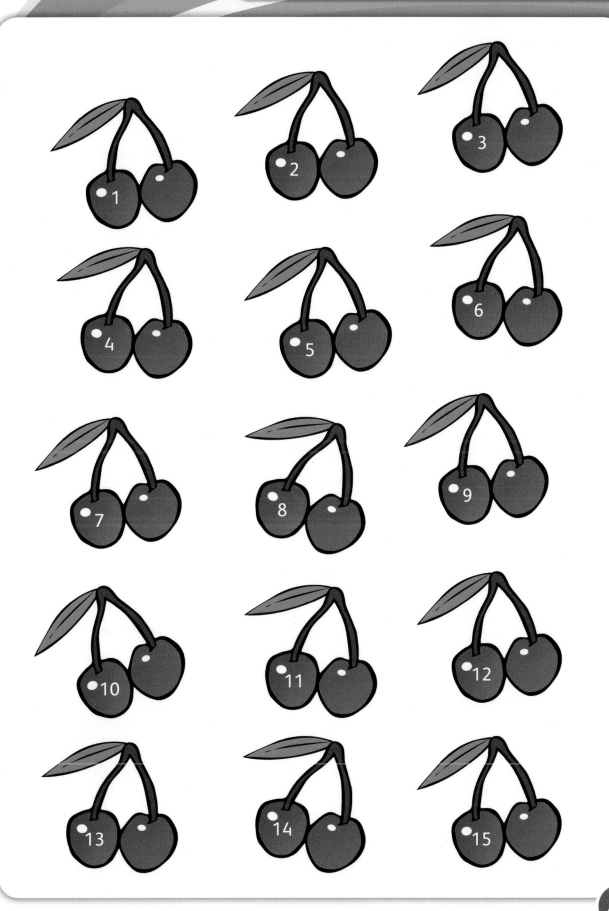

Fluency in Number Facts

Add three 1-digit numbers

Alien invasion
A game for 2 players

You need:
- 20 counters
- three 1–6 dice

Before you start:
- Place 2 counters on each flying saucer.
- Decide who has the green alien and who has the yellow alien.

Take turns to:
- roll the three dice
- add the three numbers together
- say the number sentence.

> Be sure not to cover up the number.

Golden rules
- If the answer is one of the numbers on a flying saucer, take a counter from that flying saucer and put it on one of your alien's hands.
- If there are no counters left on that flying saucer, miss that turn.
- If your answer is not on a flying saucer, miss that turn.

The winner is:
- the first player to put a counter on all 6 of their alien's hands.

Add and subtract a 2-digit number and ones

Boating bonanza: addition
A game for 2 players

You need:
- button
- two 0–9 dice: one for each player
- 10 counters: 5 for each player

What to do:
- Place the button on one of the numbers on the lifebelt.

  Be sure not to cover up the number.

- One player rolls their dice and moves the button that number of spaces around the lifebelt.

- Each player then rolls their dice and adds their dice number to the lifebelt number.

- If their answer is on any of the boats, they place a counter on that boat.

- The game continues in this way, with players taking turns to roll their dice to move the button.

Golden rules
- If both players roll the same number, both players roll their dice again.
- Each boat can only carry one counter. If a boat already has a counter on it, miss that turn.

The winner is:
- the first player to place their 5 counters on the boats.

Variation
Boating bonanza: subtraction
- Each player rolls their dice and subtracts the dice number from the lifebelt number.

Add and subtract a 2-digit number and tens

Jack-in-a-box: addition
A game for 2 players

You need:
- button
- pencil and paperclip (for the spinner)
- about 30 counters

Take turns to:
- put the button on one of the jack-in-the boxes
- spin the spinner
- add the spinner number to the number on the jack-in-a-box and say the number sentence
- find the answer on the grid and put a counter on that number.

The winner is:
- the first player to complete a line of 3 counters. A line can go sideways ⟷, up and down ↕, or diagonally ↘.

(spinner: 40 10 30 20)

Variations
Jack-in-a-box: subtraction
- Each player subtracts the spinner number from the number on the jack-in-a-box.

Jack-in-a-box: addition or subtraction
- After each spin of the spinner, the player decides whether to add or subtract the spinner number to or from the number on the jack-in-a-box.

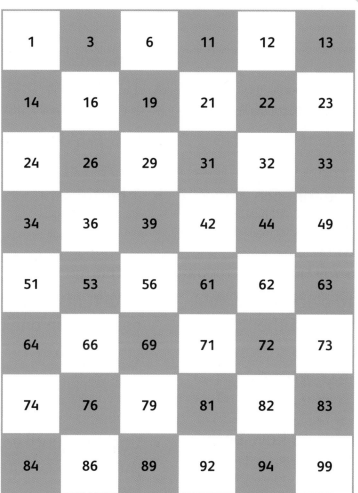

1	3	6	11	12	13
14	16	19	21	22	23
24	26	29	31	32	33
34	36	39	42	44	49
51	53	56	61	62	63
64	66	69	71	72	73
74	76	79	81	82	83
84	86	89	92	94	99

Add and subtract two 2-digit numbers

The caterpillar's boots: addition
A game for 2 players

You need:
- 16 counters: 8 of one colour, 8 of another colour
- two 1–6 dice: one for each player
- 2 buttons: one for each player

The caterpillar's boots: subtraction
A game for 2 players

You need:
- 10 counters: 5 of one colour, 5 of another colour
- two 1–6 dice: one for each player
- 2 buttons: one for each player

Before you start:
- Decide who will have which colour counters.

- Take turns to place one of your counters on one of the yellow or green leaves.

  > Be sure not to cover up the number.

- Continue until you have both put your 8 counters on 16 different leaves.

- Take turns to place one of your counters on one of the brown or yellow leaves.

  > You can only have one counter on each leaf.

- Continue until you have both put your 5 counters on the 10 leaves.

What to do:
- Each player rolls their dice and covers the matching section of the caterpillar with their button.

- Work together to add the two numbers on the boots below the covered sections.

- Work together to subtract the smaller number from the larger number on the boots below the covered sections.

50

Fluency in Number Facts

> If you both roll the same number, put both buttons on the same section of the caterpillar and add the number on the boot to itself.

> If you both roll the same number, roll both dice again.

- Remove the counter from the leaf with the answer on it.
- Keep doing this.

The winner is:
- the first player to take 5 of their 8 counters off the leaves.
- the first player to take 3 of their 5 counters off the leaves.

Recall multiplication facts for the 2 multiplication table

Toy train
A game for 2 players

You need:
- button
- 1–6 dice
- 10 counters: 5 for each player

Before you start:
- Place the button on any puff of smoke below.

Take turns to:
- roll the dice
- move the button either forwards or backwards that number of puffs of smoke
- find the 2 times-table train carriage whose multiplication matches the number the button is on
- say the number sentence and place one of your counters on that train carriage.

Golden rule
- If there is already a counter on that train carriage, miss that turn.

The winner is:
- the first player to place all their counters on 5 different carriages.

Fluency in Number Facts

Recall multiplication facts for the 5 multiplication table

Clowning around
A game for 2 players

You need
- button
- 1–6 dice
- about 24 counters

Before you start:
- Place the button on any 5 times-table ball below.

Take turns to:
- roll the dice
- move the button either forwards or backwards that number of balls
- work out the answer and place a counter on one of the balloons.

Golden rules
- You can only cover one number each turn.
- If there is already a counter on all the correct answers, miss that turn.

The winner is:
- the first player to complete a line of 4 counters. A line can go sideways ⟷, up and down ↕, or diagonally ↘.

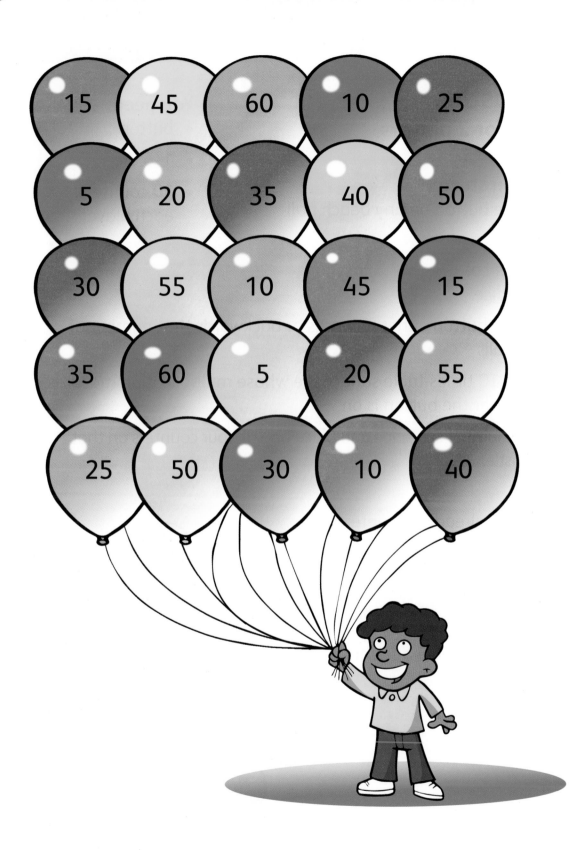

Recall multiplication facts for the 10 multiplication table

Sandcastles
A game for 2 players

You need:
- button
- 1–6 dice
- 10 counters: 5 for each player

Before you start:
- Place the button on any beach ball below.

Take turns to:
- roll the dice
- move the button either forwards or backwards that number of beach balls
- find the 10 times-table sandcastle whose multiplication matches the number the button is on
- say the number sentence and place one of your counters on that sandcastle.

Golden rule
- If there is already a counter on that sandcastle, miss that turn.

The winner is:
- the first player to place all their counters on 5 different sandcastles.

Fluency in Number Facts

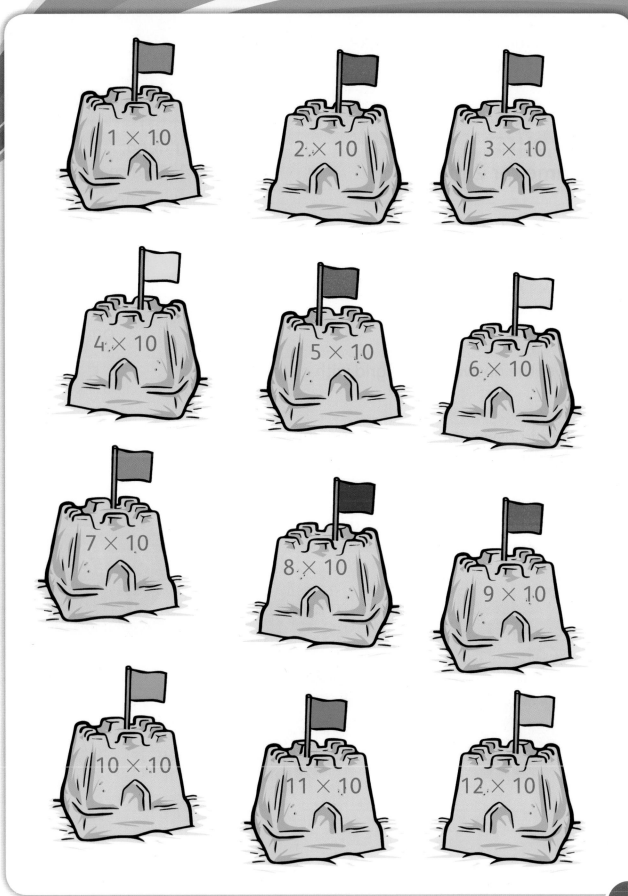

Recall multiplication facts for the 2, 5 and 10 multiplication tables

Starburst
A game for 2 players

You need:
- 1–12 dice
- about 30 counters

Take turns to:
- roll the dice
- decide whether to multiply the dice number by 2, 5 or 10
- say the times-table fact
- cover the answer on the grid with a counter.

Golden rule
- If that answer is not on the grid, miss that turn.

The winner is:
- the first player to complete a line of 4 counters, for example:

× 2

or

× 5

or

× 10

4 times 2 is 8

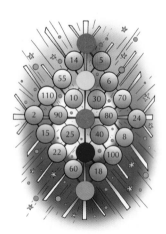

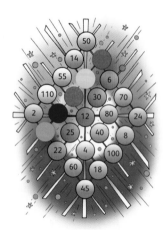

Recall division facts for the 2, 5 and 10 multiplication tables

Round the racetrack
A game for 2 players

You need:
- button
- 1–12 dice
- 10 counters

Before you start
- Decide whether you want to practise the division facts for the 2, 5 or 10 multiplication table and use that matching racetrack.

- Place the button next to the flag with that number to remind you of the division facts you are practising.

Take turns to:
- roll the dice

- find the division number sentence on the racetrack that matches the dice number

- say the number sentence and put a counter on that racing car.

Golden rule
- If the number sentence is already covered, miss that turn.

The winner is:
- the first player to complete a line of 4 number sentences, for example:

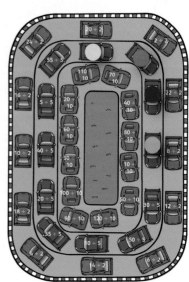

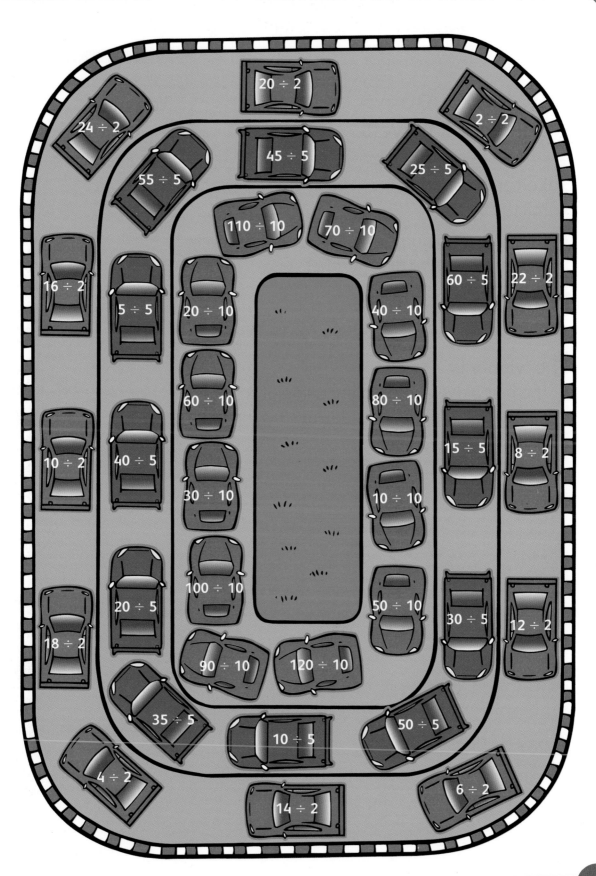

Fluency in Number Facts

Recall division facts for the 2, 5 and 10 multiplication tables

Duck division
A game for 2 players

You need:
- 1–12 dice
- 12 counters

Take turns to:
- roll the dice
- find a division number sentence on the ducks that matches the dice number
- say the division fact
- cover that number sentence with a counter.

The winner is:
- the first player to complete a line of 4 counters. A line can go sideways ←→, up and down ↕, or diagonally ↘.

$25 \div 5$ $10 \div 10$ $12 \div 2$ $40 \div 5$ $4 \div 2$ $100 \div 10$

$10 \div 2$ $60 \div 5$ $90 \div 10$ $24 \div 2$ $50 \div 10$ $15 \div 5$

$60 \div 10$ $22 \div 2$ $5 \div 5$ $30 \div 5$ $20 \div 10$ $6 \div 2$

$10 \div 5$ $110 \div 10$ $14 \div 2$ $20 \div 2$ $45 \div 5$ $70 \div 10$

$8 \div 2$ $55 \div 5$ $80 \div 10$ $40 \div 10$ $2 \div 2$ $20 \div 5$

$30 \div 10$ $18 \div 2$ $35 \div 5$ $120 \div 10$ $50 \div 5$ $16 \div 2$

Resources used in *Fluency in Number Facts* Years 1 & 2

Key domain	Game	Pages	Counters	0–9 number cards	Pencil and paperclip (for the spinner)	1–6 dice	0–9 dice	1–12 dice	Buttons
Number and place value	Which monkey wins?	24–25	•						
	Balloon numbers	26–27	•	•					
	Take the right path	28–29	•		•				
	Staircase counting	30–31	•		•				
	Courtyard counting	32–33	•			•			•
	Cover the boxes	34–35	•				•		
	Diamond grab	36–37	•				•		
Addition and subtraction	Firework additions	38–39	•				•		
	Shipwreck subtractions	40–41	•		•		•		
	Fruity facts	42–43	•				•		
	Alien invasion	44–45	•			•			
	Boating bonanza	46–47	•				•		•
	Jack-in-a box	48–49	•		•				•
	The caterpillar's boots	50–51	•			•			•
Multiplication and division	Toy train	52–53	•			•			•
	Clowning around	54–55	•			•			•
	Sandcastles	56–57	•			•			•
	Starburst	58–59	•					•	
	Round the racetrack	60–61	•					•	•
	Duck division	62–63	•					•	

How to use a spinner

Some of the paired games in this book require a spinner. This is easily made using a pencil, a paperclip and the spinner printed on each games page. Hold the paperclip in the centre of the spinner using the pencil and gently flick the paperclip with your finger to make it spin.